The DFC Library

The DFC Library

The DFC Library

BAGGAGE
TO ANGUS AND TORIN,
ENJOY THE ADVENTURE!
ALL THE BEST -
LORENZO!

BAGGAGE

A DAVID FICKLING BOOK 978 0385 61857 1

This edition published in Great Britain in 2011 by David Fickling Books,
a division of Random House Children's Books
A Random House Group Company

1 3 5 7 9 10 8 6 4 2

DAVID FICKLING BOOKS
31 Beaumont Street, Oxford, OX1 2NP

www.**kidsatrandomhouse**.co.uk
www.**rbooks**.co.uk

Addresses for companies within The Random House Group Limited can be found at: www.randomhouse.co.uk/offices.htm

THE RANDOM HOUSE GROUP Limited Reg. No. 954009

A CIP catalogue record for this book is available from the British Library.

Printed and bound in China

HUGE THANKS TO DAVID FICKLING AND HANNAH FEATHERSTONE FOR HELPING TO TRACK DOWN THE BEATING HEART OF THIS BOOK!

FICKLING
db
David Fickling Books
OXFORD · NEW YORK

FOR WILLIAM,
THE THIRD ETHERINGTON BROTHER.
WE LOVE YOU, PAL!

a comic adventure from
The ETHERINGTON BROTHERS
BAG
UP

GAGE
If found, please return to:

OUR STORY BEGINS AS THE SUN RISES OVER THE TRIPTYCH CITY TRAM STATION...

I TOOK THE RHINO FOR A LITTLE DRINK, BOSS.

RANDALL, THAT'S NOT YOUR JOB! THE ANIMAL WASN'T LOST! HE WAS WAITING TO BE COLLECTED BY THE CITY ZOO KEEPERS!
THUMP

YEAH, SURE, MR LUTZ. THAT'S ALL TRUE ... BUT HE ALSO LOOKED REALLY THIRSTY!
OH, SO NOW YOU'RE A LOST PROPERTY OFFICER AND A WILD ANIMAL EXPERT? I GUESS THAT EARNS YOU A PROMOTION, LAD.
LOST AND FOUND
I'M THE BOSS

EXCELLENT! NOW, WILL THIS PROMOTION INCLUDE A NEW UNIFORM? ONLY THIS ONE'S GOT RHINO DRIBBLE ON IT.

NO, IT WILL NOT! I WAS BEING SARCASTIC!

<SIGH> RANDALL ... JUST ... JUST TELL ME WHERE YOU TOOK THE CREATURE.
OH, NOT FAR. I LEFT HIM CHAINED TO THE WATER FOUNTAIN OUTSIDE THE TOILETS.
I'M THE BOSS

CRASHHOOM
LEFT? YOU LEFT HIM TO DO WHAT?
TO GET A HOT DOUGHNUT! THE STALL DOWNSTAIRS HAD A FRESH BATCH OF DOUBLE-GLAZED CARAMEL WONDERS. THEY'RE SIMPLY IRRESISTIBLE!
I'M THE BOSS
LOST FOUND

AND THE RHINO?
NAH. HE WASN'T HUNGRY.
I'M THE BOSS
LOST & FOUND

GAAAH! HAVE YOU ANY IDEA WHAT YOU'VE DONE TO MY TRAM STATION?

...AH...
DOUGHNUTS
Coffee
TOILETS
BLIMP ANCHOR. DO NOT RELEASE!
IT ... IT ATE EVERYTHING!. EVERYTHING EXCEPT MY HUSBAND'S PEA AND SPAM SPECIALS.
(BOY, THAT RHINO'S GOT GOOD TASTE!)

AHA. AHAHA. HA ... I CAN EXPLAIN!

GRRRRR ... RANDALL, OVER THE PAST FIVE YEARS YOU'VE CAUSED MORE ACCIDENTAL AND COLOURFUL DESTRUCTION OF PUBLIC PROPERTY THAN A LIT MATCH IN A FIREWORKS FACTORY!
RANDALL CLAY
STAFF INCIDENT REPORTS

BUT WHILST YOU'VE FOUND AMPLE TIME TO DISMANTLE OUR WORKPLACE, YOU'VE SINGLE-HANDEDLY FAILED TO LOCATE THE OWNER OF EVEN ONE ITEM OF LOST LUGGAGE!
YOIK!
WHACK

YOU MEAN YOU WANT ME TO FIND THEIR OWNERS? I THOUGHT I WAS JUST SUPPOSED TO KEEP ALL THE BAGS SAFE AND WARM AT NIGHT!!

NO! LISTEN CAREFULLY, FOR THIS IS YOUR LAST CHANCE! YOU'VE GOT UNTIL THE END OF THE DAY TO RETURN THE OLDEST PIECE OF BAGGAGE IN OUR WAREHOUSE TO ITS RIGHTFUL MASTER OR MISTRESS.
RANDALL CLAY

FAIL AND I WILL TAKE IMMENSE PLEASURE IN REPLACING YOU WITH A CARDBOARD CUT-OUT! NOW ... SCRAM!
YIKES! YES, SIR!

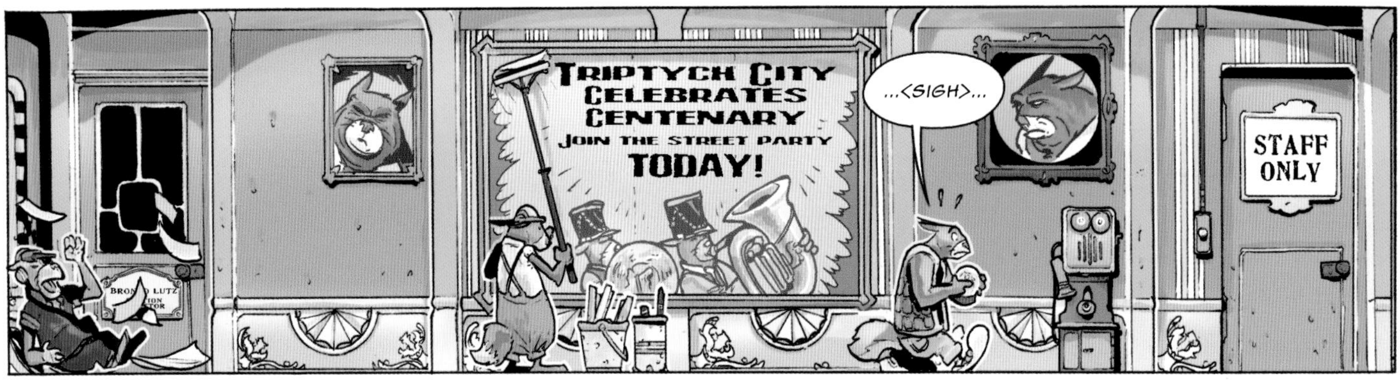
TRIPTYCH CITY
CELEBRATES
CENTENARY
JOIN THE STREET PARTY
TODAY!
...<SIGH>...
STAFF
ONLY

IT BEATS ME WHY BRONCO'S ALWAYS SO ANGRY. IF I OWNED THE TRAM STATION I'D BE AS HAPPY AS A PIG IN *POOP.*

ALL HE DOES IS SHOUT. AND SETTING ME THIS IMPOSSIBLE TASK IS JUST **MEAN.**
STAFF
EXIT
HOT DOGS
WARM DOGS
& CHILLY DOGS

ONIONSKINS
SEASON FINAL!
KICK OFF 7PM
AT THE
VEG
BOWL!
I'VE NEVER EVEN SEEN THE OLDEST THING IN OUR WAREHOUSE ... *YEEESH* ... IT COULD BE **ANYTHING.**

TAKE THAT OFF YOUR HORN, SILLY, AND DON'T LOOK AT ME LIKE ***THAT.*** YOUR APPETITE JUST GOT ME IN A LOT OF TROUBLE!

BLIMP
ANCHOR.
DO NOT
RELEASE!
WHY DO THESE THINGS ALWAYS HAPPEN TO ME? IT'S NOT LIKE IT'S EVER **MY** FAULT...

WELL, HERE WE ARE. THESE DOORS NEVER FAIL TO IMPRESS!
LOST PROPERTY WAREHOUSE
RULE NUMBER 1: NEVER OPEN ITEMS OF LOST LUGGAGE.
RULE NUMBER 2: SEE RULE NUMBER 1
RULE NUMBER 3: WASH YOUR HANDS AFTER PICKING UP LUGGAGE OR PICKING YOUR NOSE.
RULE NUMBER 4: SEE RULE NUMBER 2
RULE NUMBER 5: NO SLEEPING ON DUTY – AND THAT MEANS YOU, RANDALL!
RULE NUMBER 6: SEE RULE NUMBER 4
THINGS THAT STACK NICELY
THINGS THAT HAVE MORE THAN THREE WHEELS
HMMM ... PERHAPS THE BOSS HAS GOT A POINT. THIS PLACE IS GETTING A LITTLE ON THE FULL SIDE!
LOST AND FOUND
THINGS THAT ARE REALLY QUITE DANGEROUS

THINGS THAT SMELL FUNNY
THINGS ARE
THINGS THAT ARE AN AMUSING SHAPE
OKAY, SO LET'S THINK. WHERE WOULD I FIND THE OLDEST THING? I PROBABLY SHOULD HAVE ADDED A DATE COLUMN TO MY FILING SYSTEM.
THINGS THAT MIGHT NOT ACTUALLY BE LOST
ERM, EXCUSE ME. I THINK THERE'S BEEN SOME SORT OF MISTAKE!
LOST & FOUND
TOOBA

THINGS THAT WOULD MAKE A NICE CHRISTMAS PRESENT
<PHEW!> I'M GETTING NEAR THE END OF THE LINE. IT MUST BE JUST AROUND...
THINGS THAT NEED TO BE WATERED DAILY
THINGS THAT TICK WHICH AREN'T BOMBS
TOSS
CANDY FLOSS

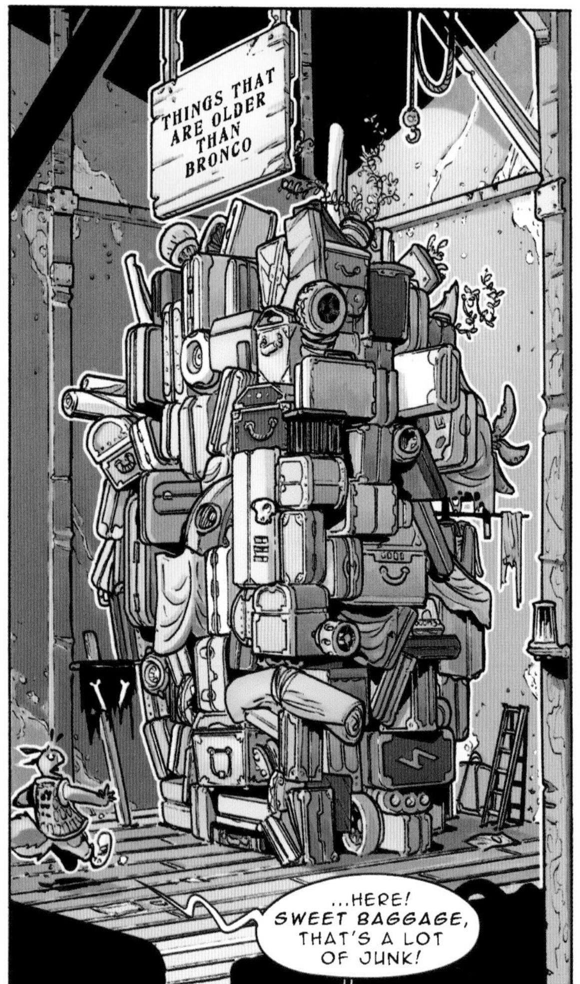
THINGS THAT ARE OLDER THAN BRONCO
...HERE! SWEET BAGGAGE, THAT'S A LOT OF JUNK!

IF THIS IS ALL THE STUFF THAT'S BEEN LOST THE LONGEST, THEN I GUESS WHATEVER IS AT THE BOTTOM MUST BE...

...THE OLDEST OF THE BUNCH!
LOST & FOUND

OUT YOU COME, PAL ... <NGGN> IT'S YOUR LUCKY DAY!

<NEEEEGH> RESISTANCE IS USELESS! <NGG> YOU'RE LEAVING WITH ME AND THAT'S THAT!

WOOOAH!
PLOP

UH-OH! I REALLY DIDN'T THINK THAT THROUGH!

NOT GOOD,
NOT GOOD!

NOT GOOOOOD!
LOST & FOUND

YOWZER!
WHAMMPH

BOOOOOOOM
SNACKS

YOIK!
NARK!
OICH!
BOINK
THUMP

NOW THIS ... THIS IS PROBABLY THE SORT OF THING THAT BRONCO WOULD DESCRIBE AS COLOURFUL DESTRUCTION.

AAGH! RANDALL!

LITTLE CASE, I DON'T KNOW IF YOU CAN HEAR ME, BUT THAT WAS OUR CUE TO LEAVE!

DECISIONS, DECISIONS...
TRIPTYCH TRAM STATION
TRAM, FERRY & CABLECAR TIMETABLE
1 2 3
4 5 6
7 8 9
A B C
REFRESHMENTS THIS WAY
TOILETS

PERFECT! THE *DOUBLE* IS JUST ABOUT TO LEAVE! BRONCO WILL NEVER CATCH ME!
TRAM ROUTE 3
CALLING: AUTUMN DAZE, BOULDER DRIVE, SUGAR PALM SPA, MARBLE ROW, JUNKTON MARKET & QUAYSIDE.
DEPARTS: 06:57 07:57 08:57 09:30 10:15
THEN EVERY 45 MINUTES UNTIL THE DRIVER GETS BORED AND GOES HOME FOR HIS DINNER.

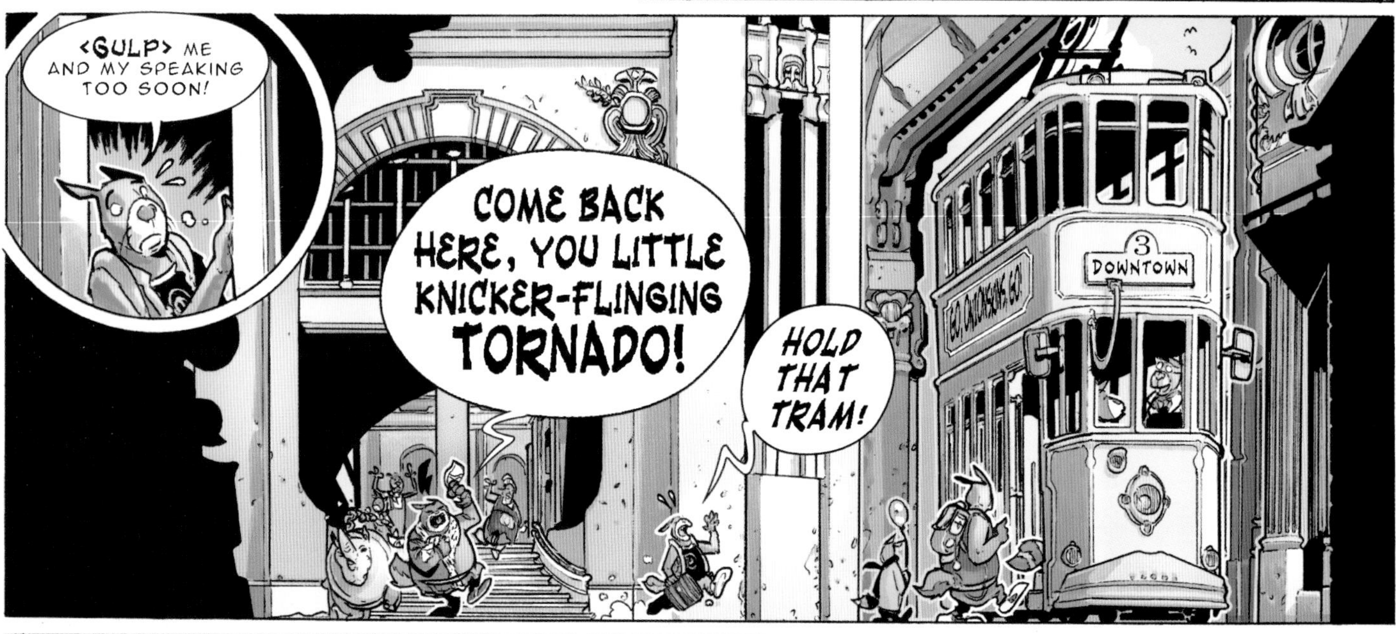
<GULP> ME AND MY SPEAKING TOO SOON!
COME BACK HERE, YOU LITTLE KNICKER-FLINGING TORNADO!
HOLD THAT TRAM!
3
DOWNTOWN

NSKINS, GO!
3
DOWNTOWN
HOP
SKIP

IS THERE A REASON, YOUNG RANDALL, WHY OUR BOSS IS CHASING AFTER YOU WITH AN ARMFUL OF UNDERWEAR?
HI, ABE! ER, NOPE ... NOT THAT I CAN THINK OF! NOW CAN WE PLEASE GO!

ALL ABOARD!
DESTINATION, DOWNTOWN AND INDUSTRIAL!

YES!

NO ONE IN MY FAVOURITE SEAT AND BRONCO DIDN'T GET TO STRANGLE ME WITH SOME STRANGER'S LONG-LOST UNDERWEAR!

PERHAPS MY LUCK IS CHANGING...
STAMP
THUMP

HMMM...

HOW I'D LOVE TO KNOW WHAT'S INSIDE THIS THING ... BUT THAT WOULD BE BREAKING THE RULES!
RATTLE
AH, YOU CAN'T BE WORRYING ABOUT EVERY LITTLE DETAIL IN LIFE, RANDALL. THAT KIND OF STRESS IS BAD FOR YOUR HEALTH. JUST LOOK AT BRONCO - EVEN HE WAS HAPPY ONCE.

REALLY, ABE? SO TELL ME - IS DRIVING THE TRAM A LITTLE DETAIL!
NO, THAT'S ACTUALLY PRETTY SERIOUS.

WHAT? WHAT IS IT? WHY ARE YOU LOOKING AT ME LIKE THAT?.

OH, YEAH, OKAY - I'LL GO BACK TO OPERATING THE BIG LEVER THAT STOPS US FROM CRASHING INTO THE RIVER.
I THINK WE'D ALL APPRECIATE THAT!

NOW THEN, LET'S HAVE A GOOD LOOK AT MY LONG LOST COMPANION.
ELEPHANT STOMP
OnioN SkinS
a castle i wud like to liv in
OAKTON Park
Where MOTHER NATURE HANDS OUT THE HUGS
I-SPY
THE FUTURE IS NOW
OnioN SkinS
THE VEG BOWL
GOLD MEMBERS PASS 38
HOME OF THE ONION SKINS
TRIPTYCH CITY ZOO
OnioN SkinS

WOAH, LITTLE CASE, YOU'VE BEEN EVERYWHERE! YOUR OWNER MUST HAVE REALLY LOVED THE CITY.

THERE'S A NAME UNDER HERE - 'H. BENNINGTON'. COOL, MY FIRST CLUE! WELL, MR BENNINGTON, IF YOU'RE STILL LIVING IN TOWN...

...I'M COMING TO FIND YOU!
GO, ONIONSKINS, GO!
AUTUMN DAZE RETIREMENT VILLAGE

WEHEHE ... ONE, PLEASH! HEHEHE...

WHEHEHEHE...
?

'SHCUSE ME, FELLA, DO YOU MIND IF I SIT DOWN?
ER ... NOPE, I GUESS NOT.

HEHEHE ... ISHN'T IT GOOD TO GET AWAY FROM **THEM** ALL!
DON'T YOU MEAN 'GET AWAY FROM **IT** ALL?'

DAZE
ETIREMENT
VILLAGE
HEY! COME BACK!
NOT TODAY! WHEHEHEHE!
GO, ONIONSKINS, GO!

DOWNTOWN SHOPPING
THIS WAY
THE SPICE IS RIGHT
GRINDING PEPPER SINCE 1902
SHO, LIDDLE FELLA, OFF SHOMEWHERE NICE?

I'M SORRY?
THE **BAG**. YOU'RE OFF ON YOUR HOLIDAYSH, RIGHT?
TAP TAP

OH, NO, NO! HA, THIS ISN'T EVEN *MINE*!
AH. **SHTOLEN.** NOW I UNDERSHTAND.

SHHHH! DON'T SAY THINGS LIKE THAT!
DON'T WORRY, FELLA. I WON'T TELL!

WHAT WON'T YOU TELL?
ABOUT YOUR **LIFE OF CRIME!** YOUR SHECRET ISH SHAFE WITH ME!

WELL NOW, THIEF, WOULD YOU TAKE A GANDER AT THAT...

ELEPHANT SHTOMPSH! I HAVEN'T SHEEN OR HEARD OF THAT BRAND IN A LOOOONG TIME!
ELEPHANT STOMP
CHEWING GUM
"STOMP 'EM IF YA GOT 'EM"

IS IT REALLY THAT OLD?

SHURE! I LIVED OFF FIVE PACKSH OF SHTOMPS A DAY FOR ABOUT TWENTY YEARSH, SHAME ASH EVERY OTHER KID!

NO WORD OF A LIE! THAT CHEWING GUM'SH WHAT GAVE ME THISH WONDERFUL SHMILE!

YEEESH!
UH-HUH!

AND YOU ALWAYSH USED TO GET FREE SHPORTS CARDSH INSIDE ... AND THERE WAS THISH GREAT JINGLE THAT THEY PLAYED ON THE RADIO! HOW'D IT GO...
3
DOWNTOWN
STOP
STOP

SHCRUNCH, SHCRUNCH, SHCRUNCH YOUR GUM SHPEEDILY DOWN THE SHTREAM, SHTOMPY, SHTOMPY, SHTOMPY, SHTOMPY ELEPHANT GUM'SH A DREAM!

WHEHEHEHE! IT USHED TO SHOUND A LOT BETTER WITH MY TEETH.

NO ARGUMENTS HERE. SO WHERE DID YOU GO TO BUY THIS GUM?
HA, WELL, THE KIDSH MIGHT HAVE LOVED IT, BUT THE MAYOR HAD A PROBLEM WITH ALL OUR TEETH FALLING OUT. HE BANNED THE SHTUFF. THE ONLY PERSHON WHO MANAGED TO SHMUGGLE PACKSH INTO THE CITY WAS RUBY BEE!
DABBY DAB
PROPERTY OF

SHE'S SHTILL GOT HER LITTLE SHTORE JUSHT DOWN HERE ON THE CORNER. BEEN THERE FIFTY YEARSH.
DING
DING
GO, ONIONSKINS, GO!

THANKS, MISTER. AND I HOPE YOU ENJOY YOUR HOLIDAY.
I'M NOT ON HOLIDAY EITHER - JUSHT BROKE OUT OF THE OLD FOLKSH HOME AND I'M NOT GOING BACK! WHEHEHE!
PROPERTY OF AUTUMN DAZE RETIREMENT VILLAGE

HEHE! OH, SILLY, YOU MEAN GREAT GRANNY, THE ORIGINAL RUBY BEE! SHE'S OUT BACK MOULDING LIQUORICE INTO RUDE SHAPES. I'LL GO AND GET HER.

<AHEM> ... THAT WAS EMBARRASSING.

...INCREDIBLE...

COCOA A-HOYS!
CANDY MAN CANCANS
MONKEY NUTS
TRIPLE BRITTLE RIPPLES
CHOCO DIPPA NANA
KING CRUNCH
CRUMBLE POPSTOPPERS
I HAVEN'T FELT EVEN A LITTLE BIT PECKISH SINCE THIS MORNING'S DOUGHNUT ... BUT A WALL OF CHOCOLATE CAN HAVE A FUNNY EFFECT ON A BOY!

YUK! AND JUST LIKE THAT, MY APPETITE'S GONE!
WOOF!
WHITE CHOCOLATE WITH CHEDDAR & GARLIC!

YOU CAN BUY IT OR YOU CAN PUT IT BACK, SONNY! BUT YOU CAN'T PLAY WITH IT!

RANDALL, THIS IS-
YEAH, YEAH, I CAN SPEAK FOR MYSELF. I'M THE RUBY BEE, OWNER OF THAT BAR YOU'VE GOT YOUR MITTS ON.
WHAT - OH, SORRY! UM, MA'AM, I WAS WONDERING IF YOU COULD HELP ME WITH SOMETHING?
KOOKY COOKIES
LOST AND FOUND

WHY SURE! IF YOU'RE HAVIN' DIFFICULTY MAKIN' A CONVINCIN' BUM OUT OF LIQUORICE THEN I'M YOUR LADY.
NO, NO, NOTHING AS COMPLICATED AS THAT!

MY BOSS, BRONCO, HAS ASKED ME TO FIND THE OWNER OF THIS SUITCASE. THEY MIGHT HAVE BEEN A FAN OF THE ELEPHANT STOMPS GUM YOU USED TO SELL.

BRONCO, EH? THAT MOODY OLD GROUCH USED TO BE SUCH A HAPPY BOY. WELL, I'D LOVE TO HELP BUT I'VE NEVER SEEN THIS GRUBBY THING BEFORE. WHAT'S RATTLING AROUND IN THERE?
NO IDEA - I'M NOT ALLOWED TO OPEN LOST LUGGAGE, MA'AM. BUT THERE'S A NAME UNDERNEATH. H. BENNINGTON.
RATTLE

HUBERT BENNINGTON!

GRANNY... YOU CAN WALK?!
OF COURSE! YOU KNOW, THAT BENNINGTON BOY BOUGHT MORE STOMPS THAN ANY OTHER CHILD IN THE CITY! USED TO VISIT ME EVERY WEEK, WITHOUT FAIL. SOMETIMES TWICE A WEEK.

'COURSE, WITH ALL THE CITY CELEBRATIONS GOIN' ON, HALF THE STREETS ARE BLOCKED. YOU'RE GOIN' TO HAVE TO TAKE THE DOCKLAND TRAM SOUTH TO RAVENSWOOD, THEN SWITCH TO THE TWO HILL BRIDGER, BUT UNFORTUNATELY THEY ONLY RUN ON THE SECOND TUESDAY OF EACH MONTH, SO INSTEAD YOU'D BETTER WALK BACK NORTH-WEST, CROSS THE HAYSEED MARKET AND UP ALPHABET AVENUE TILL YOU REACH THE PELT 'EM PIE PALACE...

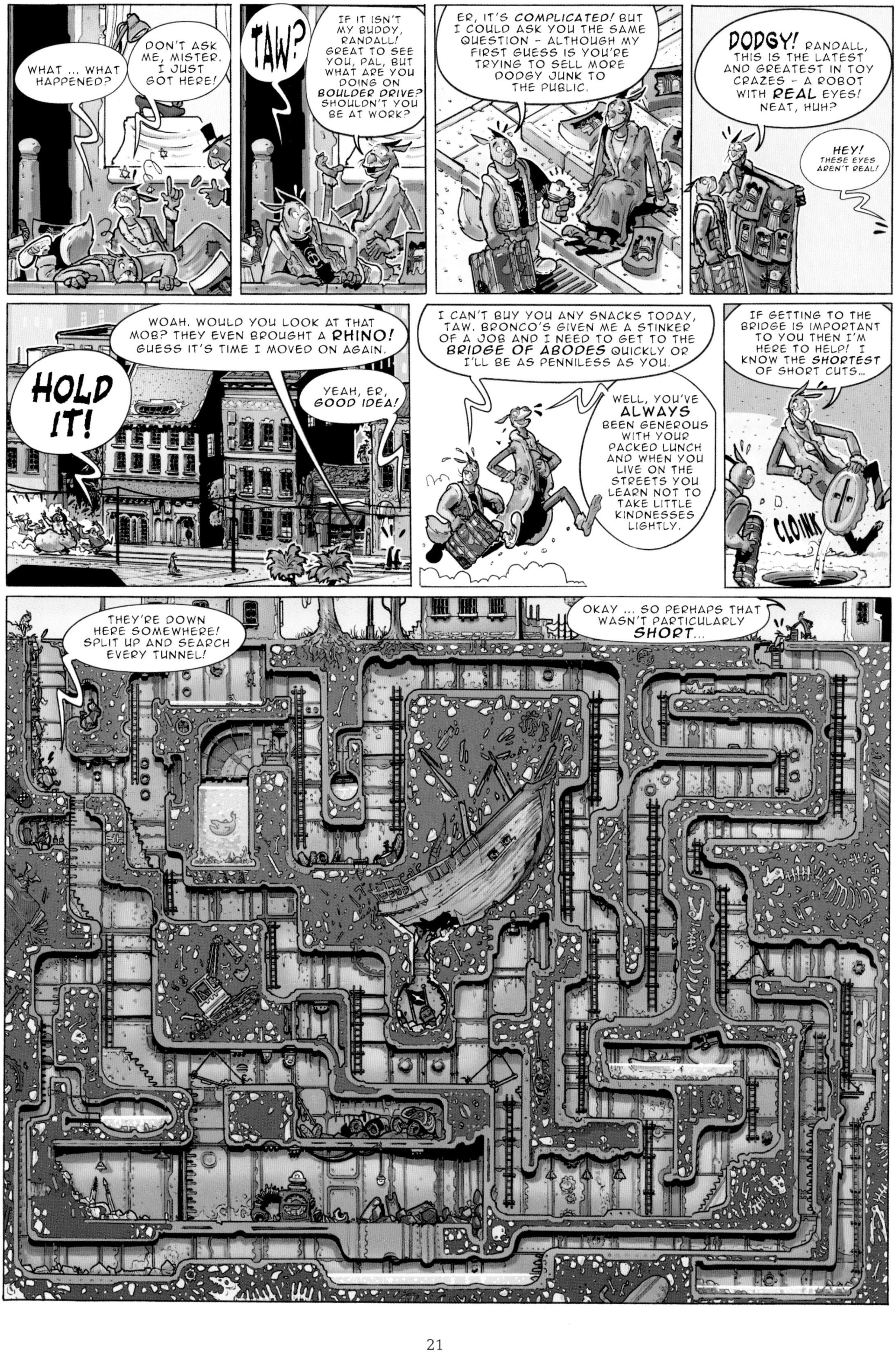

IF GETTING TO THE BRIDGE IS IMPORTANT TO YOU THEN I'M HERE TO HELP! I KNOW THE SHORTEST OF SHORT CUTS...

CLOINK

THEY'RE DOWN HERE SOMEWHERE! SPLIT UP AND SEARCH EVERY TUNNEL!

OKAY ... SO PERHAPS THAT WASN'T PARTICULARLY SHORT...

THE BRIDGE OF ABODES
...BUT WE GOT HERE IN THE END!
THAT WE DID, TAW. NOW TELL ME IF YOU CAN SPY A POSTBOX MARKED 'BENNINGTON'.

SECONDS LATER
WHAT ... LIKE THIS ONE?
LOST & FOUND

EXACTLY LIKE THAT! GOOD SPOT!
SEE, THIS IS WHY I'M TRYING TO GET FOLKS TO ADOPT MY NEW NICKNAME: 'LUCKY!'
TAP TOC
BENNINGTON

YOU CAN'T GIVE YOURSELF A NICKNAME. THAT'S NOT HOW IT WORKS.
BUT OTHER PEOPLE CALL ME THINGS LIKE "TRAMPY", "NO SHOES" AND "CHEATING, STINKY LITTLE SWINDLER". I'VE BEEN TRYING FOR SOMETHING MORE UPBEAT...

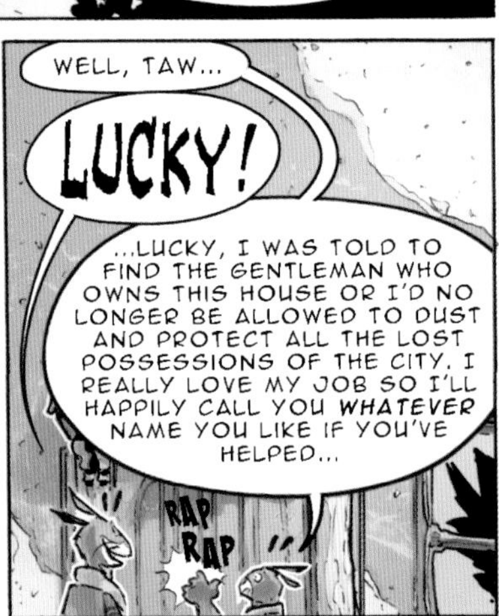
WELL, TAW...
LUCKY!
...LUCKY, I WAS TOLD TO FIND THE GENTLEMAN WHO OWNS THIS HOUSE OR I'D NO LONGER BE ALLOWED TO DUST AND PROTECT ALL THE LOST POSSESSIONS OF THE CITY. I REALLY LOVE MY JOB SO I'LL HAPPILY CALL YOU WHATEVER NAME YOU LIKE IF YOU'VE HELPED...
RAP RAP

...BRING MY TASK TO AN ... END?
WUMP

I'M GETTING THE DISTINCT FEELING MR BENNINGTON ISN'T ABOUT TO GREET US WITH A DRINK AND A BISCUIT.
'COURSE HE ISN'T! HAHA! THIS HOUSE HAS BEEN EMPTY FOR YEARS! HAHAHA!

WHAT? WHY DIDN'T YOU SAY SOMETHING WHILE I WAS KNOCKING?
BECAUSE I WAS HOPING THE ROTTEN DOOR WOULD COLLAPSE ... AND IT DID! HEHEHE!

AH, DON'T SCREW YOUR FACE UP, PAL. YOU LOOK LIKE A BULLDOG WITH A ROTTEN TOOTH CHEWING ON A WASP WRAPPED IN BARBED WIRE.
VERY POETIC. NOW ARE YOU COMING TO HELP ME POKE AROUND UPSTAIRS OR WOULD YOU RATHER STAY HERE AND GIGGLE TO YOURSELF?

IS THAT A REAL CHOICE?

HEY, SOMEONE'S BEEN LIVING HERE ... BUT NOT FOR A WHILE. THIS FIRE'S OLD.
YEAH, <AHEM>, YOU COULD BE RIGHT ABOUT THAT.

I DON'T THINK THERE'S MUCH POINT ROOTING THROUGH THIS LOT. LOOKS LIKE WE'VE HIT A DEAD-END.
UM, MAYBE WE SHOULD JUST TAKE A QUICK PEEK IN HERE. YOU, ER, NEVER KNOW!

OKAY ... (BUT I WOULDN'T GET MY HOPES UP, LITTLE PAL.)

WHAT DO YOU THINK THAT'S SUPPOSED TO BE?
I'VE ABSOLUTELY NO IDEA! AND I CAN'T IMAGINE HOW IT GOT BROKEN! <COUGH>

WEIRD. I WONDER WHAT A 'PEEWEE' IS...
~PEEWEE~ STAR OF THE ONIONSKINS

HMMM ... THE OUTLINE IN THIS CASE LOOKS JUST LIKE A SHIRT—
ARE WE FINISHED? WE'RE FINISHED, RIGHT? ONLY I THINK I NEED A LITTLE FRESH AIR! AH ... AND A BITE TO EAT! YES, AND—
CRIK
CREEEEAK

CALM DOWN, TAW! WHAT'S GOT INTO YOU—
ER, RANDALL?...
SNAP
KRAKKETY

WOAH!
KOOMPH

GRAB
GOTCHA!
MY TAIL! THE ROBOTS!
LET ME GO - I MUST SAVE MY BABIES!

WELL, THERE'S GRATITUDE! NEXT TIME I'LL GIVE YOU A PUSH.

ONE GRUBBY ESCAPE LATER
COUGH!
HAK!

THOSE DOLLS OF YOURS CERTAINLY KICKED UP A LOT OF DIRT.
THEY WEREN'T DOLLS! THEY WERE COLLECTABLE ROBOTS!
TAP TAP

OH WELL, EASY COME, EASY GO! NO USE CRYING OVER SPILT EYES. EVEN IF THEY WERE VERY REALISTIC.
GLAD YOU CAN SEE THE BRIGHT SIDE OF THINGS, PAL. BUT I'M SORRY FOR YOUR LOSS.

WELL, IF YOU REALLY WANT TO MAKE ME FEEL BETTER YOU CAN BUY US BOTH SOMETHING TO WASH THE DUST FROM OUR THROATS!
I AM IN KIND OF A HURRY ... BUT, OKAY. SURE. WHAT DID YOU HAVE IN MIND?
A TRIP TO A LITTLE PLACE I LIKE TO CALL ... PARADISE!

MINI MICA'S
FLOATING DUCK
OUR ICES ARE NICE AND OUR SHAKES ARE GREAT!
HEY THERE, LUCKY! WHAT'S UP?
<YOU HEAR THAT? SOMEONE LIKES MY NEW NAME!>

SWEET MICA, MEET MY BUDDY, RANDALL. THE MILKSHAKES ARE ON HIM!
LOST & FOUND

SO, RANDALL, THIS CHARMING GUY HAS GOT HIS HOOK INTO YOU TOO, HUH?
LOST & FOUND
SNAG

'LUCKY' IS A GREAT FRIEND, MICA. UNLESS YOU'RE ONE OF HIS CUSTOMERS, AND THEN HE'LL VANISH AS SOON AS YOUR BACK IS TURNED!
LOST & FOUND
POINK

!?!

MY THOUGHTS EXACTLY!

FLOATING DUCK
OUR ICES ARE NICE AND OUR SHAKES ARE GREAT!
ALMOST THERE...
WE'RE ... WE'RE MOVING?! WHAT'S GOING ON?

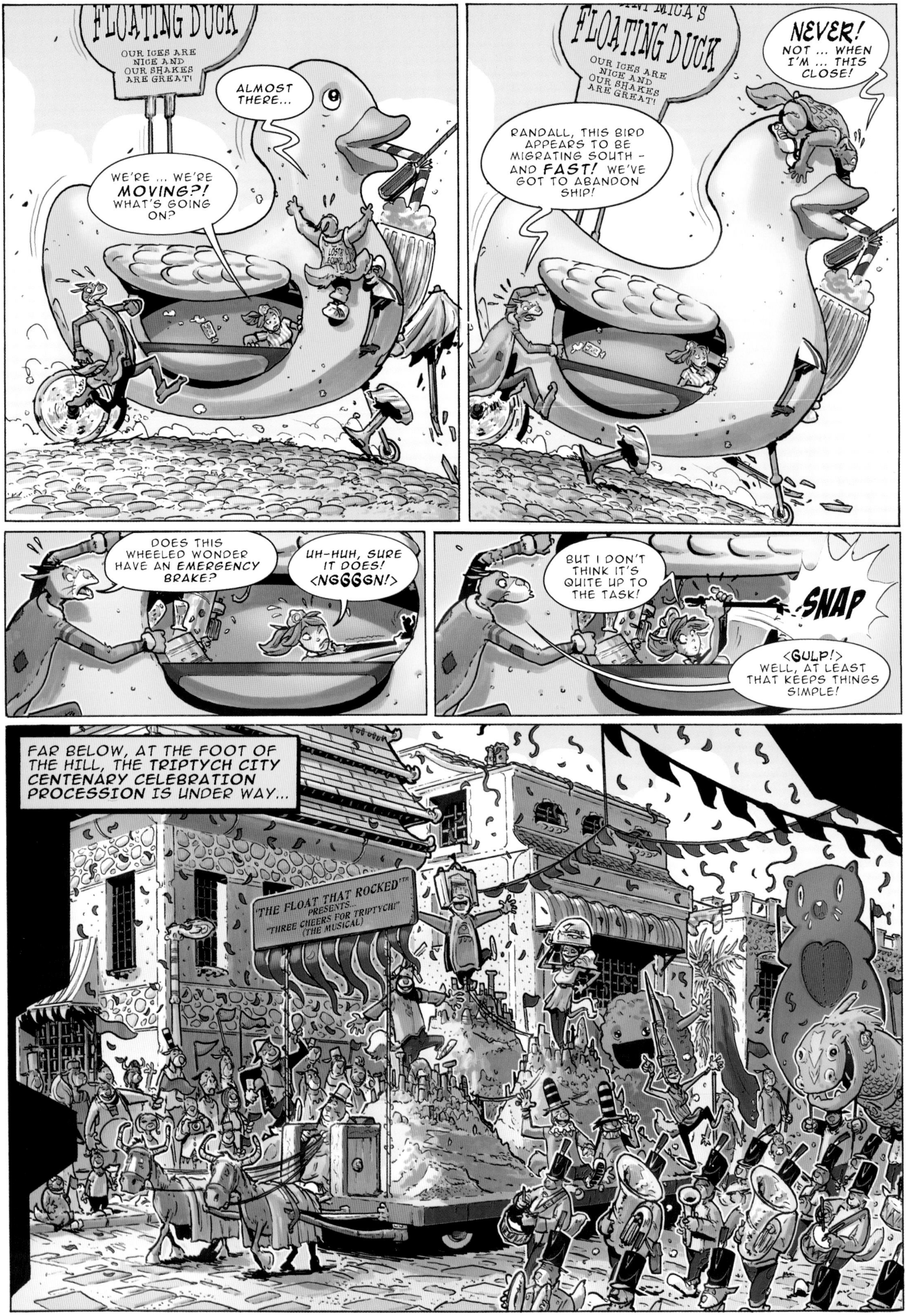

FLOATING DUCK
OUR ICES ARE NICE AND OUR SHAKES ARE GREAT!
RANDALL, THIS BIRD APPEARS TO BE MIGRATING SOUTH – AND FAST! WE'VE GOT TO ABANDON SHIP!
NEVER! NOT ... WHEN I'M ... THIS CLOSE!

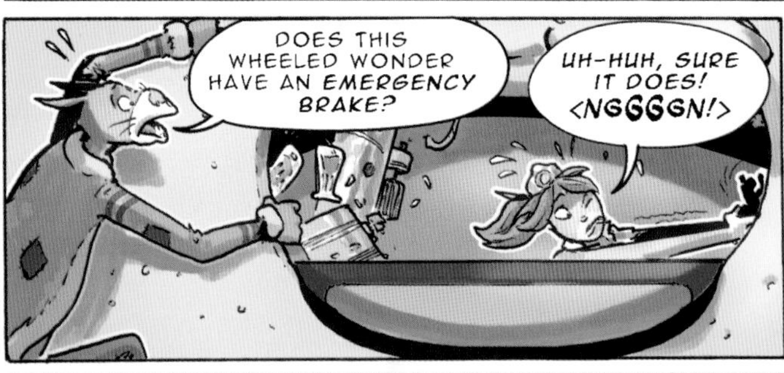
DOES THIS WHEELED WONDER HAVE AN EMERGENCY BRAKE?
UH-HUH, SURE IT DOES! <NGGGGN!>

BUT I DON'T THINK IT'S QUITE UP TO THE TASK!
SNAP
<GULP!> WELL, AT LEAST THAT KEEPS THINGS SIMPLE!

FAR BELOW, AT THE FOOT OF THE HILL, THE TRIPTYCH CITY CENTENARY CELEBRATION PROCESSION IS UNDER WAY...
"THE FLOAT THAT ROCKED"™ PRESENTS... "THREE CHEERS FOR TRIPTYCH!" (THE MUSICAL)

AGH!

MOVE! MOVE! MOVE!
GET OUT THE WAY!
QUICKLY, BEFORE-

<SIGH> ...NEVER MIND...
YOOMPF

THE CASE!

SORRY!
PARDON ME!
JUST PASSING THROUGH!
HOP
TUMP

IT'S IMPOSSIBLE, RANDALL! THAT ROPE'S TOO HIGH TO REACH!
OH, FORGET THE STUPID BAG AND LOOK WHAT'S HAPPENED TO MY POOR CART!

TAW, YOU'RE RIGHT! I'LL NEVER GET IT FROM HERE...
LOST FOUND

I NEED MORE ELEVATION!

BINGO!

GET UP HERE, LUCKY! I THINK I KNOW HOW YOUR DAFT FRIEND IS PLANNING TO ESCAPE!
HE'D BETTER MAKE IT QUICK! THE NATIVES ARE GETTING A TOUCH RESTLESS!

THOSE THREE BUMS HAVE RUINED THE CELEBRATIONS! DON'T LET THEM GET AWAY!

HEY! ONLY ONE OF US IS A BUM AND PERSONALLY I RESENT THAT TERM! 'HOMELESS' WILL DO JUST FINE!
STOP NEGOTIATING, HOLD ON TO MY HAND AND GET READY!

THE WIND'S CHANGING! THE CASE IS COMING BACK!
HUP!
HUP!

HHHNNNGG!

GOTCHA!

WOAH ... DID WE REALLY CAUSE ALL THAT?
YOU DID! NOW SWING CLOSER ... CLOSER ...

JUMP!

<GAH!> TOO HEAVY! MY HANDS ARE SLIPPING! WE NEED TO FIND SOMEWHERE TO TOUCH DOWN!
ER, THAT LITTLE PROBLEM IS ABOUT TO TAKE CARE OF ITSELF...

SLAM
WHAM

<COUGH!> THIS DAY IS STARTING TO GET AWAY FROM ME ... LIKE A JOKE WITHOUT A PUNCH-LINE. STILL, AT LEAST WE'VE GOT THE CASE BACK.

MORE IMPORTANTLY YOU'RE BEGINNING TO SEE THE POSITIVE SIDE OF LIFE, BUDDY - AND THAT'S NO LAUGHING MATTER!

Visit TRIPTYCH CITY ZOO
IF YOU'RE RIGHT, WHAT'S THAT LITTLE GIRL GIGGLING AT?
BEATS ME - WHO UNDERSTANDS WHAT KIDS FIND FUNNY?
BWAHAHA!

IS ANYONE GOING TO EXPLAIN WHAT'S GOING ON? I'M ALMOST AFRAID TO ASK, BUT WHAT'S IN THIS CASE? WHAT COULD POSSIBLY MERIT THIS MUCH MAYHEM?
I HONESTLY DON'T KNOW! LOST PROPERTY OFFICERS AREN'T ALLOWED TO LOOK INSIDE LOCKED LUGGAGE.

I'M SORRY, MICA, THINGS ARE GETTING OUT OF CONTROL. YOU SHOULD SNEAK AWAY. TAW, IS THE COAST CLEAR?
I WOULDN'T USE THOSE EXACT WORDS...

...AND THEN THEY STOMPED ON OUR PAPIER-MACHÉ MODEL OF THE OBSERVATION NEEDLE!
SACRILEGE!

WE MUSTN'T GET CAUGHT! WE MUSTN'T GET CAUGHT! BRAVE LITTLE CASE, WE'VE COME TOO FAR!
RANDALL, YOU REALLY SHOULD CALM DOWN. MAYBE EAT SOMETHING. I ALWAYS EAT WHEN I'M NERVOUS!

GOOD IDEA! THIS OLD GUM RUBY GAVE ME MIGHT DO THE TRICK!

GUYS - I THINK I'VE FOUND US THE PERFECT PLACE TO LAY LOW!

WOW! ~RARE STUFF~
OKAY, BUT WE STILL HAVE TO GET ACROSS THE STREET WITHOUT BEING SPOTTED.
HA - LEAVE THAT TO ME!

STRANGE ... HOW CAN THEY HAVE ESCAPED?
GRRR! THEY HAVEN'T! TRASH LIKE THAT PAIR DON'T SIMPLY WALK AWAY!
WOW! RARE STUFF

I DON'T WANT TO CRITICIZE YOUR CLEVER PLAN, LUCKY, BUT DO YOU THINK YOU SHOULD HAVE CUT SOME EYE-HOLES IN THIS BIN?
EYE-HOLES?
...<CHEW>... EYE-HOLESH?

?!?
TRIP

WHAMM

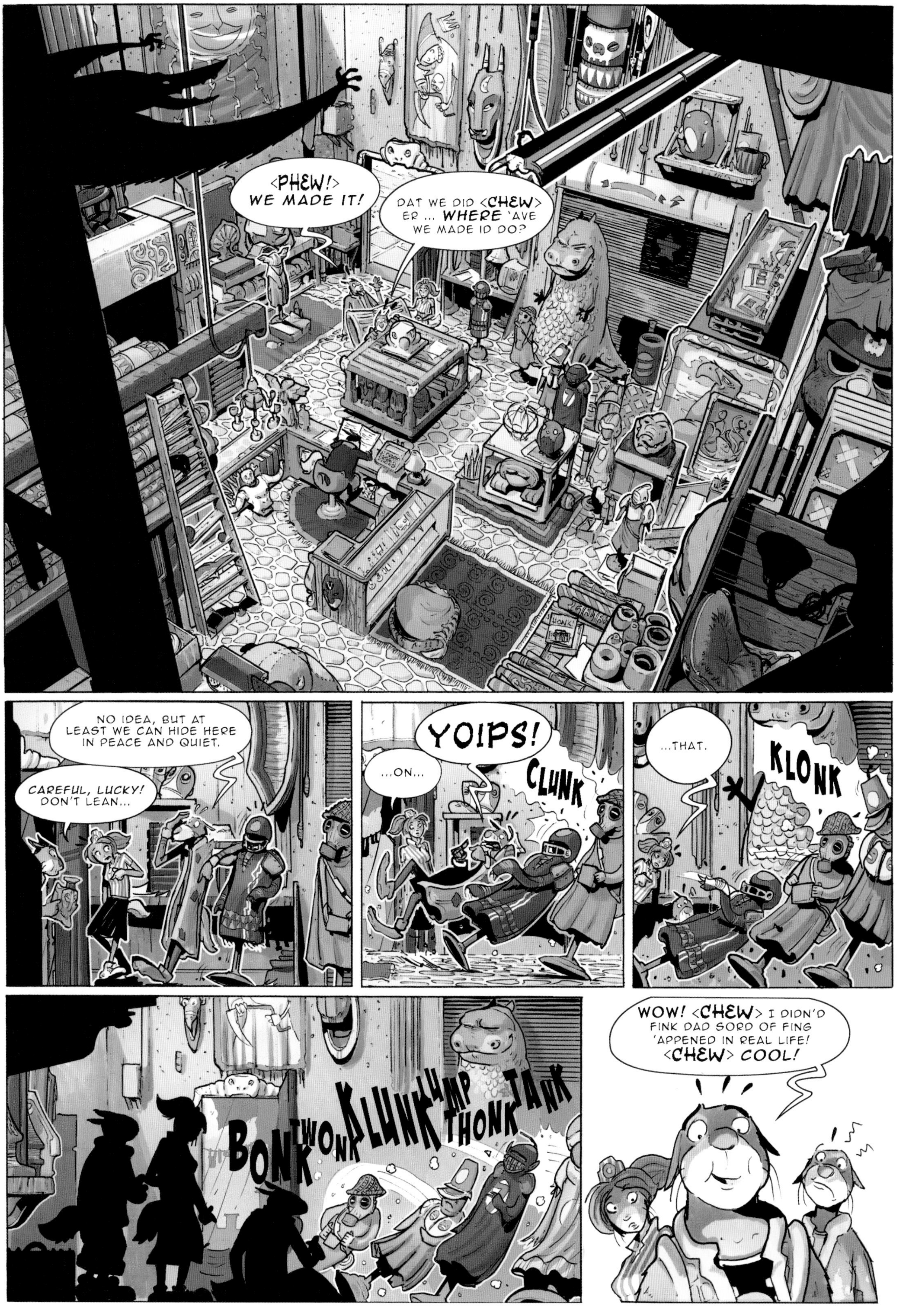

<PHEW!> WE MADE IT!
DAT WE DID <CHEW> ER ... WHERE 'AVE WE MADE ID DO?

<CHEW> WE NEED DO FIND OUD MORE ABOUD DIS FING!

POOR CHAP ... BY THE SOUND OF IT HE'S GOING TO NEED FILLINGS.

DOING A SPOT OF REDECORATING, FEN?
VERY FUNNY, KONG!

NOW WHERE WAS I?...

MY WORD, I'VE NEVER SEEN SO MANY LUGGAGE LABELS!
ZZZZZZ-* ...SNARK... ...GRRWWWL?

WHOEVER OWNED THIS THING CERTAINLY LIKED TO SEE THE SIGHTS!
YEAH. AND THEY WERE A PRETTY BIG SPORTS FAN. LOOK AT ALL THE ONIONSKINS STICKERS.

ER, RANDALL? NEED A HAND THERE, PAL?

GOODNESS ... THAT IS A GOLD MEMBERS PASS! BUT THAT MEANS THIS CASE MUST BELONG TO SOMEONE WITH A-

SAY, HOW MUCH FOR THE HOLD-ALL, FEN? MY CRUSHED CARPETBAG IS GETTING A LITTLE WORN.
SORRY TO SAY, KONG, BUT I DON'T THINK THIS CASE IS FOR SALE.

A RIVAL COLLECTOR, EH? GOOD - KONG LIKES A CHALLENGE! NOW WHAT'S INSIDE THIS THING...
SHAKE

OIF!

GRWWWWWWWWL!

GET OFF MY BACK!

ROOOOWF!

YOU FOOLS! YOU'VE WOKEN THE BEAST! RUN! RUN FOR YOUR PENNILESS LIVES!

SMAASH

WAIT FOR US!

ROOOOWF!
WATCH OUT!

RANDALL, THAT ANIMAL LOOKS MIGHTILY PEEVED!
AGREED! I THINK WE'D BETTER FOLLOW ITS MASTER'S ADVICE AND RUNNNNNN!

SNARRRRL!

LET ME GO! PUT ME DOWN!
OH, HOW I WISH I COULD!

COME BACK, LUCKY! YOU'RE GOING THE WRONG WAY!
HOW CAN AWAY-FROM-THE-TERRIFYING-HOUND BE THE WRONG WAY?

THAT'S HOW!
YIKES!

!?!

WE'RE TRAPPED! THAT RABID MONSTER'S GOING TO CHEW US TO A PULP!
HEY, I DIDN'T CHOOSE THE NICKNAME 'LUCKY' FOR NOTHING! THE CATS-EYE CABLE CAR IS JUST ABOUT TO LEAVE!

CORRECTION - IT'S ALREADY LEFT!
FERRY
BUT, BOYS, IF WE WAIT ONE MINUTE WE CAN GET ON THE-

SORRY, MICA! THERE'S NO WAITING ON THIS ADVENTURE!

AAAAAAAAAH!

WHAMP
GOIF!

THUMP

HEHE, NICE LANDING, MISTER KONG! HAVING FUN?
NO, YOU HAIRY LUNATIC! AND IF I WASN'T STUCK TO THE BACK OF THIS IMBECILE I'D BOP YOU BOTH IN THE MOUTH!

WELL THEN, IT'S A GOOD THING THAT YOU ARE STUCK!
HUH? WHERE DID MICA GO?

SHE'S A CLEVER GIRL, TAW. PROBABLY PICKED THE PERFECT MOMENT TO LEAVE US. THIS HOPELESS HUNT IS BRINGING NOTHING BUT BAD LUCK!
DON'T LOSE HEART, BUDDY! YOU'RE DOING A GREAT JOB ... BUT THAT SAID, I THINK WE SHOULD PREPARE FOR ANOTHER HASTY DEPARTURE.
CHUFF CHUFF

SURE, SURE. SOON AS THE CABLE CAR STOPS.

IN AN IDEAL WORLD, YES, THAT'S WHEN WE'D GET OFF. BUT LIKE MOST THINGS TODAY, THE MATTER MIGHT BE OUT OF OUR HANDS!

WHAT ARE YOU TRYING TO SAY, TAW? JUST SPIT IT OUT!

THE ROOF, RANDALL! THIS RAIN IS MAKING IT SLICK AND IT'S GETTING SLICKER BY THE SECOND!
<GULP!>, OKAY, SO WE DON'T MOVE! WE STAY AS STILL AS-

GURK!
SHUT UP! ENOUGH! LET ME OFF!
WRIGGLE

STOP ROCKING, KONG! YOU'LL SEND US OVER THE EDGE!
YOU'RE HOLDING ME PRISONER! I KNOW MY RIGHTS!

RANDALL!
HELP ... I'M ... I'M SLIPPING!
YOU CAN'T OPPRESS THE SMALL! FREEDOM FOR ALL! SAY NO TO ILLEGAL CAPTIVITY!

NOOOOO!
...OH NO...

AAAAAAAGH!
CHUFF
CHUFF

RANDALL! I ... I COULDN'T SAVE HIM ... I FAILED...

WOAH! YIP! STEADY! STEADY!
SKIT
SKIPTY

BUMS!
SLIP

SORRY, KONG, BUT I THINK WE'RE DONE FOR!
ONLY IF WE HIT THE WATER! AIM FOR THAT GARBAGE BARGE!

?!

KRAPPOOMPH
CHUFF
CHUFF

<CAK> SAVED BY THE UNWANTED FILTH OF THE CITY! <GAG> THERE'S PROBABLY A MORAL IN HERE SOMEWHERE BUT I'M NOT SEARCHING FOR IT!

AT LEAST WE'RE FINALLY FREE! THINGS COULDN'T POSSIBLY GET ANY WORSE...
OH, THAT'S JUST GREAT! JINX US, WHY DON'T YOU?

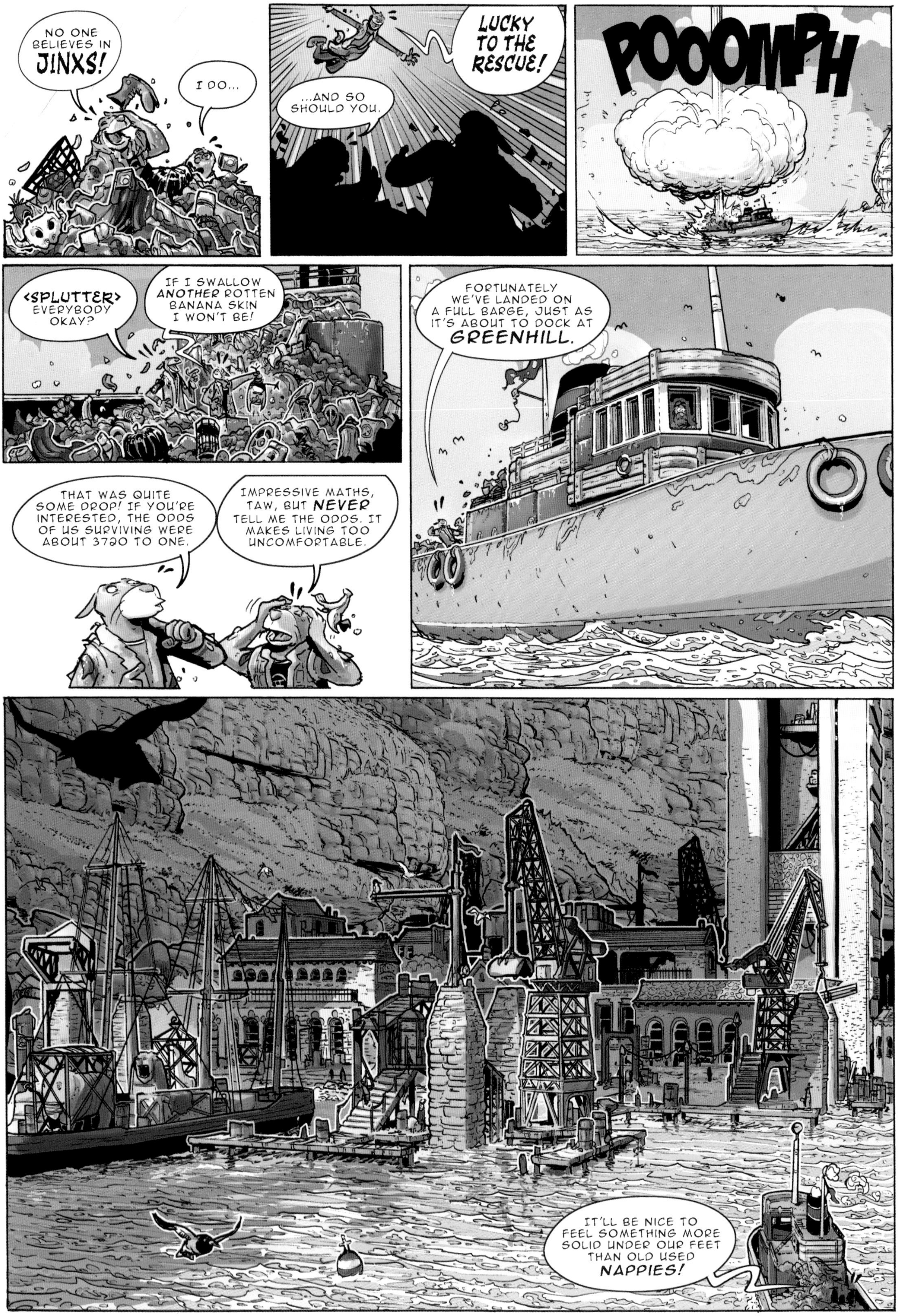

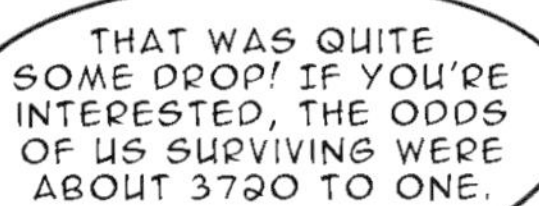

IT'LL BE NICE TO FEEL SOMETHING MORE SOLID UNDER OUR FEET THAN OLD USED NAPPIES!

HEY! WEIRDOS!
WHAT DO YOU THINK THIS IS - A PUBLIC SWIMMING POOL?

WELL, UM...
AH, YES...

IT'S ALL A SIMPLE MISUNDERSTANDING, CAPTAIN! A CASE OF A LOST CASE...

...WHICH WE'VE NOW REACQUIRED!
PLOP

SO IF YOU'D BE GOOD ENOUGH TO SET US DOWN GENTLY, I WON'T PRESS CHARGES FOR THE DAMAGE TO MY CLOTHING.
I BEG YOUR PARDON?!

<SHHH> DON'T PUSH IT, KONG! LET'S JUST GET TO SHORE...
WHAT'S MORE, I HAVE A SUSPICION THAT THIS BARGE IS OVERLOADED! I SHOULD PROBABLY REPORT YOU, BUT I'M FEELING GENEROUS.

YOU'RE FEELING GENEROUS, ARE YOU, SUNSHINE? WELL, SO AM I! IF YOU WANT TO BE SET DOWN...

...IT'LL BE MY PLEASURE!
!?!

KLANG

SWIIING

AAAGH!

OKAY, MOB - SPREAD OUT! THOSE TROUBLESOME IDIOTS ARE SOMEWHERE ON GREENHILL SO KEEP YOUR EYES PEELED!
WELL, AT LEAST WE'RE ON DRY LAND!
TAW, IS YOUR OLD COAT ACTUALLY MADE FROM SILVER LININGS?
COULD BE! NOW LET'S GO BEFORE THAT CAPTAIN HITS US WITH ANOTHER LOAD!
GAH! THIS ... THIS DISASTER IS ALL YOUR FAULT, BAG BOY!
OKAY, THE CHEWING GUM WAS ENTIRELY MY ERROR BUT...
DON'T LISTEN TO HIM, RANDALL. KONG'S JUST UPSET BECAUSE HE GOT HIS NATTY BRACES IN A GRUBBY TWIST. HE CAN'T SEE HOW MUCH FUN WE'RE HAVING!
THERE THEY ARE...
FUN? YOU CALL THIS FUN! I'M GOING TO FLATTEN YOUR PUG-FACED MUG!
STICKS AND STONES MIGHT BREAK MY BONES BUT NOTHING WILL STOP ME CELEBRATING OUR RANDOM DAY OF ADVENTURING AND DERRING-DO!
SPLOOOSH
<BLUB> N-NOTHING?
NOPE - NOT EVEN A TIDAL WAVE OF DIRTY RAIN WATER!
?!

WELL, I'M GLAD TO SEE YOUR FORTUNES HAVE NOT IMPROVED IN MY ABSENCE.
MICA? HOW DID YOU- WHY DID YOU-

THE HOW IS EASY, LUCKY. AS I TRIED TO EXPLAIN, THE FERRY WAS DUE TO LEAVE TWO MINUTES AFTER THE CABLE CAR! AS FOR THE WHY ... I WAS WORRIED SOMETHING MIGHT HAPPEN TO YOU.
<OH, TAW, SHE IS A VERY CLEVER GIRL! PRETTY TOO...>
YES ... PRETTY...
PLUCK

STAND ASIDE, RANDALL! ROMEO AND I NEED TO HAVE A LITTLE CHAT!
GO EASY ON HIM, KONG! DON'T DO ANYTHING I MIGHT REGRET WATCHING!

WHAT IS THIS?
UM ... MY CHEST?

I'M TALKING ABOUT THE CHAMPIONSHIP JERSEY YOU'RE WEARING! HOW DID YOU COME TO POSSESS THIS UNIQUE TREASURE?!

ER!... WOULD YOU BELIEVE I SIMPLY FOUND IT? AHA!
NO, WE WOULD NOT! YOU'RE NOT THAT LUCKY!

OKAY, OKAY ... SO MAYBE I SPENT LAST CHRISTMAS IN THE ABANDONED BENNINGTON HOUSE AND, ER, AND MAYBE I BROKE INTO THAT GLASS CASE WE FOUND IN THE BEDROOM AND TOOK THE SHIRT THAT WAS HANGING THERE!

DON'T LOOK AT ME LIKE THAT! I DIDN'T KNOW WHAT ELSE TO DO! I WAS FREEZING!

I COULD CARE LESS!

LOOK - THIS SHIRT BELONGED TO THE FAMOUS PEEWEE! INCREDIBLE!
URK!
PEE WEE

PEEWEE WAS THE ONIONSKINS' MOST SUCCESSFUL PLAYER OF ALL TIME! HE'S A LEGEND!
HEY, MY LOST CASE IS COVERED IN ONIONSKIN STICKERS ... DO YOU THINK THERE'S A CONNECTION?
ONLY THAT YOUR LUGGAGE AND THAT SHIRT BELONG TO A SERIOUS SPORTS FAN - MUCH LIKE MYSELF!

KONG, I NEED YOUR HELP - WHERE WOULD I FIND SUCH A SUPER FAN? IF I DON'T RETURN THIS CASE BEFORE NIGHTFALL, BRONCO'S GOING TO EAT ME ALIVE.
YOU WORK FOR BRONCO?! OH, THAT MAN IS ONE GRUMPY LUMP! YOU'D BETTER FOLLOW ME, RANDALL - THE END OF YOUR SEARCH IS CLOSE AT HAND! WE HEAD FOR THE VEG BOWL STADIUM!
OOMERS
PRETTY BLOOMERS
OAKTON
PARK

OAKTON PARK
HEY, GUYS! WAIT UP A SEC...
OKAY, BOYS, THE MOB IS ALL YOURS. THE PARK STINKS OF RASCALS AND WRONGDOING, SO LEAVE NO LEAF UNTURNED! I'M OFF TO BED...

WHAT'S ON YOUR MIND?

I FEEL REALLY BAD ABOUT TAKING THIS SHIRT. I'M NO THIEF! YOU'VE GOT TO BELIEVE ME!
OF COURSE I DO. THIEVES DON'T SMILE AS OFTEN AS YOU!
AND IT WAS A HORRIBLY COLD WINTER.

BUT NEXT TIME YOU'RE CHILLY, JUST CALL ME. I'VE ALWAYS GOT A SPARE JUMPER OR TWO THAT COULD USE A GOOD HOME.
YOU'RE A TRUE FRIEND, RANDALL.

BOY, I LEAVE YOU LOT FOR ONE MINUTE AND YOU LOSE ALL SENSE OF FOCUS!

WE'VE ARRIVED! NOW ALL WE NEED TO DO IS PURCHASE A COUPLE OF TICKETS AND WE'RE HOME...
THE VEG BOWL

...FREE. AH.
THE VEG BOWL
· SEASON FINAL ·
SOLD OUT!
TICKETS
NOTHING'S EVER EASY, IS IT?

YOU FOUR - OVER HERE!
TICKETS
HUH? WHO, US?

I CAN SPOT DISAPPOINTED BIG GAME SUPPORTERS A MILE OFF! IT JUST SO HAPPENS THAT I HAVE HERE A HANDFUL OF RESERVED TICKETS THAT ARE GOING BEGGING!
BUT THAT'S GREAT NEWS! HOW MUCH ARE THEY?

USUALLY $15 A PIECE, BUT FOR YOU VALIANT SPORTS FANS THEY'RE... STILL $15! WAHAHA! MY LITTLE JOKE!

HAR DE HAR HA. ALRIGHT, WE'LL TAKE THEM.
NO WE WON'T, BUDDY. I'VE A FEELING YOU MIGHT HAVE LEFT YOUR CASH IN THE WRECKAGE OF MICA'S DESTROYED MILKSHAKE CART.

WORRY NOT - I'M HAPPY TO COVER THE COSTS...

HMMMM... THAT'S STRANGE...
RUMMAGE

IT'S GONE! GREAT GODS! I MUST HAVE DROPPED MY WALLET WHILE PADDLING UP TO MY EARS IN OTHER PEOPLE'S STINKY CRUD!

SECURITY! I'VE GOT A 'SHOUTER' AT BOOTH THREE!
WHAT? WHAT DID I SAY?

LEAVE THE TICKETS, KONG! THERE'LL BE ANOTHER WAY INSIDE.

BLIMEY, IT'S GETTING LATE! BRONCO'S PROBABLY ALREADY HIRING MY REPLACEMENT...
I'D OFFER MY SYMPATHIES, BUT THAT POSTER IS MAKING ME TOO HUNGRY TO CARE!
MEATY MEATBALLS SPONSOR THE ONIONSKINS
TICKETS
?

RANDALL, CAN WE GET SOME MEATY MEATBALLS? PLEASE?
HEHE! PERFECT!
MASCOTS ONLY

LUCKY, IF IT'S MEATBALLS YOU'RE AFTER THEN I'VE JUST DISCOVERED THE JACKPOT.
WOO-HOO! LET ME AT 'EM!

ERM ... THAT'S NOT QUITE WHAT I HAD IN MIND.
WOW ... MICA, YOU'RE A MARVEL!
I AGREE WITH BAG BOY! WHAT AN INTREPID IDEA!

TODAY HAS CERTAINLY HAD ITS MOMENTS.
YUK! MY COSTUME IS ALL ITCHY.
HUNTED BY A BRASS BAND, CHASED BY A MAD DOG, ALMOST DROWNED ON A RUBBISH BARGE AND THIS IS WHAT BOTHERS YOU, TAW?
ONIONS FOR THE CHOP!
ONIONSKINS 4 EVER!
REAL ONION FANS DON'T CRY!
GO, MELON FARMERS!
OKAY, EVERYONE, JUST TRY TO BLEND IN!

MELONS RULE!
BETTER A MELON THAN AN ONION!
GO, GO MELONS GO!
ONIONS FOR THE CUP!
ALL MY FRIENDS ARE MELON FARMER FANS!
SNACKS!
ONIONSKINS

HEHEHE! IT'S A WALKING DO-DO!
GET OFF ME, KID!
OKAY, KONG, WE'RE IN, BUT THE CLOCK'S STILL TICKING! WHAT ARE WE LOOKING FOR?
IT'S NOT A WHAT BUT A WHO! THE VEG BOWL STADIUM HAS BEEN HOME TO THE ONIONSKINS TEAM FOR CENTURIES.

AND ONE PERSON HAS BEEN HERE A VERY LONG TIME! THEIR CURRENT COACH...

...OXBLOOD JACKSON!
WHAT PART OF TACKLE DO YOU NOT UNDERSTAND, STEELY? YOU'VE HEARD ME USE THE WORD IN TRAINING, YES?
YEAH, ERM, IT'S WHEN WE TRY TO STOP THE OTHER GUYS FROM SCORING ANY POINTS! USUALLY BY KICKING THEM HARD IN THE WHATNOTS!

TEXTBOOK DEFINITION, SON! NOW GET OUT THERE AND TACKLE!
SURE THING, BOSS!
BAM

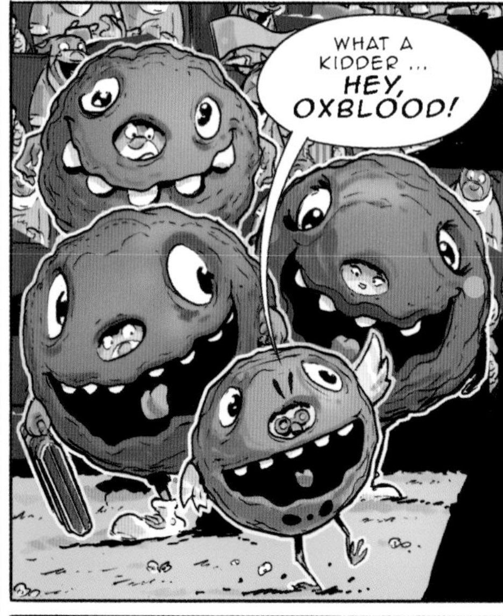
WHAT A KIDDER ... HEY, OXBLOOD!

WHAT DO YOU LOT WANT?
IT'S AN HONOUR TO MEET YOU TOO, SIR!

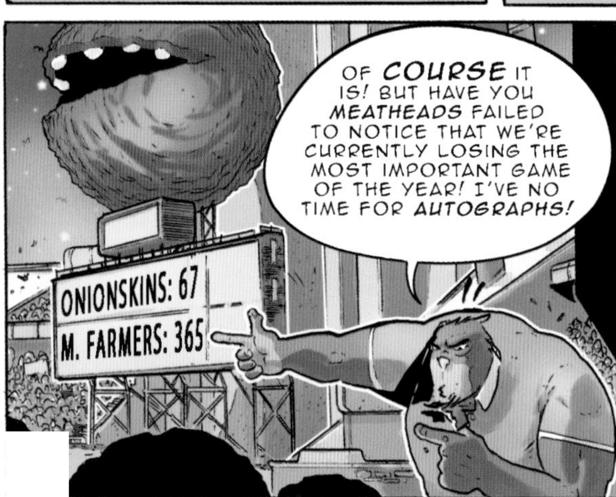
OF COURSE IT IS! BUT HAVE YOU MEATHEADS FAILED TO NOTICE THAT WE'RE CURRENTLY LOSING THE MOST IMPORTANT GAME OF THE YEAR! I'VE NO TIME FOR AUTOGRAPHS!
ONIONSKINS: 67
M. FARMERS: 365

SORRY, MR JACKSON, BUT THIS IS REALLY URGENT! WE'RE TRYING TO TRACK DOWN AN ONIONSKINS FAN.

ONE FAN? HA! LOOK AROUND YOU, SON. YOU'RE SURROUNDED BY THOUSANDS AND THEY ALL LOOK THE SAME TO ME.

IF YOU CAN READ THIS YOU'RE NOT WATCHING THE GAME!
A MELON IN THE HAND IS WORTH TWO ONIONS ON THE PITCH!
YEAH! MELONS!
ONIONSKINS!
MELON!
'FRAID THERE'S JUST NO WAY TO FIND A NEEDLE IN THIS HAYSTACK.

BUT WHAT ABOUT YOUR LIFETIME MEMBERS? DO THEY GET ANY SORT OF SPECIAL TREATMENT?
GOLD MEMBERS PASS 38
HOME OF THE ONION SKIN

THE LIFERS? YEAH, SURE. THEY GOT THEIR OWN PLUSH BOX UP THERE - BEST SEATS IN THE HOUSE!

ARE YOU LOOKING FOR A LIFER? WELL, I SHOULD TELL YOU THEY'RE PRETTY MUCH ALL BUT GONE NOW.

WHAT ABOUT NUMBER 38? HUBERT BENNINGTON. WHERE DOES HE SIT?
H.BENNINGTON

DEAR OLD HUBERT! WHAT A CHARACTER. YOU KNOW HE DESIGNED THE ROOF OF THIS STADIUM. REMINDS ME OF A SNOW GLOBE...

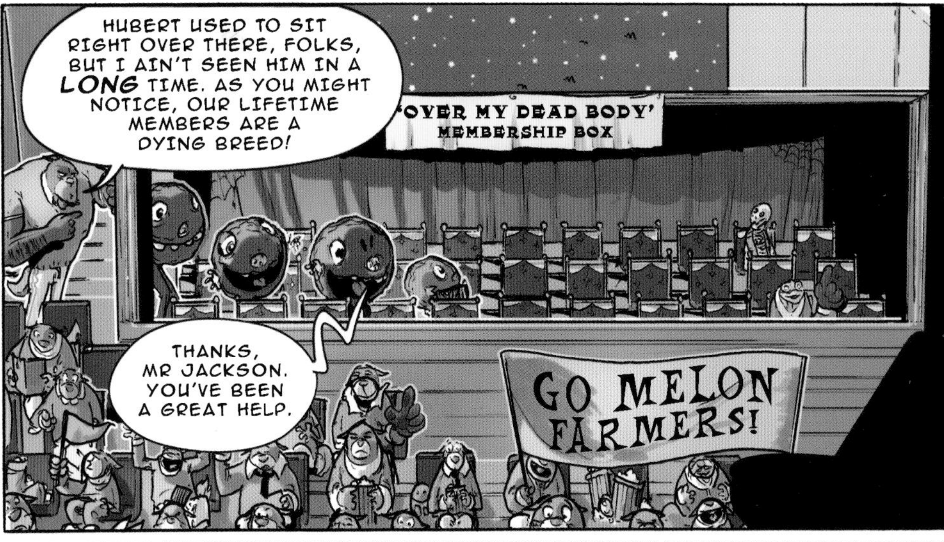
HUBERT USED TO SIT RIGHT OVER THERE, FOLKS, BUT I AIN'T SEEN HIM IN A LONG TIME. AS YOU MIGHT NOTICE, OUR LIFETIME MEMBERS ARE A DYING BREED!
'OVER MY DEAD BODY' MEMBERSHIP BOX
THANKS, MR JACKSON. YOU'VE BEEN A GREAT HELP.
GO MELON FARMERS!

AH, FREEDOM! WHOEVER WORE THIS LAST MUST'VE HAD FLEAS!
HUH?
HMM ... NO SIGN OF HUBERT BUT THERE'S SOMETHING SCRATCHED INTO SEAT 38 ... "FUTURE PROPERTY OF-"

AND WHO EXACTLY ARE YOU, SON? I DON'T RECOGNIZE THAT GOOFY MUSH!
<GULP> AHA! YES, I'VE JUST, ER, JOINED THE MASCOTS, SIR! VERY KEEN TO LEARN THE MEATBALLS DANCE ROUTINE! UM ... DO THEY HAVE A ROUTINE?

NO - THEY DON'T! SOUND THE ALARM! FAKE BALLS IN THE BOWL!

UH-OH! LOOKS LIKE OUR COVER'S BLOWN!
YOUR COVER YOU MEAN! DO YOU TWO ACTUALLY GO **LOOKING** FOR TROUBLE?
NO, BUT IT HAS A NASTY HABIT OF FINDING US! COME ON – WE CAN **ARGUE** ON THE MOVE!

THOSE FLEEING FOOLS MUST BE MELON SPIES! TACKLE THEM, BOYS – **TACKLE HARD!**
(BUT BRING THE COSTUMES BACK IN ONE PIECE ... THEY TOOK ME AGES TO SEW!)

CRUSH 'EM!
MINCE 'EM!
KICK 'EM IN THE WHAT-NOTS!

MY MEATBALL IS WEIGHING MY HEAD DOWN!
WHERE ARE WE GOING **NOW**, RANDALL?
I'M NOT REALLY SURE, BUT I BET THE EXITS ARE GOING TO BE BLOCKED AND GUARDED!

ALL MY FRIENDS ARE MELON FARMER FANS!
ONSKI
ONIONSKI
WHAT WE REALLY NEED IS A **HUGE** DISTRACTION...

THERE THEY ARE!

!?!

SEVERAL 'MEMORABLE' MOMENTS LATER

WHAM

BOP

THUMP

SMACK

MELONS RULE, OK!

ONIONSKINS FOREVER!

HALF TIME SNACKS

CHAAAAAAAAARGE!
PLEASE DON'T!

?!?

KRUNTCH

CREEEEAK
ONIONSKINS: 67
M. FARMERS: 365

THOSE MUPPETS DESTROYED THE SUPPORTS – THE SCOREBOARD'S COMING DOWN!

THIS IS THE SECOND TIME TODAY I'VE BEEN THREATENED BY A LARGE COLLAPSING STRUCTURE!

WHAT A DILEMMA ... HOW'S THE REFEREE GOING TO HANDLE THIS ONE?

ABANDON GAME!
ABANDON PITCH!
ABANDON STADIUUUUUUM!
ONIONSKINS: 67
M. FARMERS: 365

KA-BOOM

WOULD YOU LOOK AT THAT...
TUMMBLE

EVERY YEAR, VITRO, WE HOPE LIKE HECK FOR A TRULY EXCITING END TO THE SEASON. THIS MIGHT BE ONE FOR THE RECORD BOOKS!
I DON'T NORMALLY BELIEVE IN THE POWER OF SUBLIMINAL ADVERTISING, PRIT, BUT I KNOW WHAT I'M HAVING FOR DINNER!
PRIT SKITTLES
VITRO KIBBLER

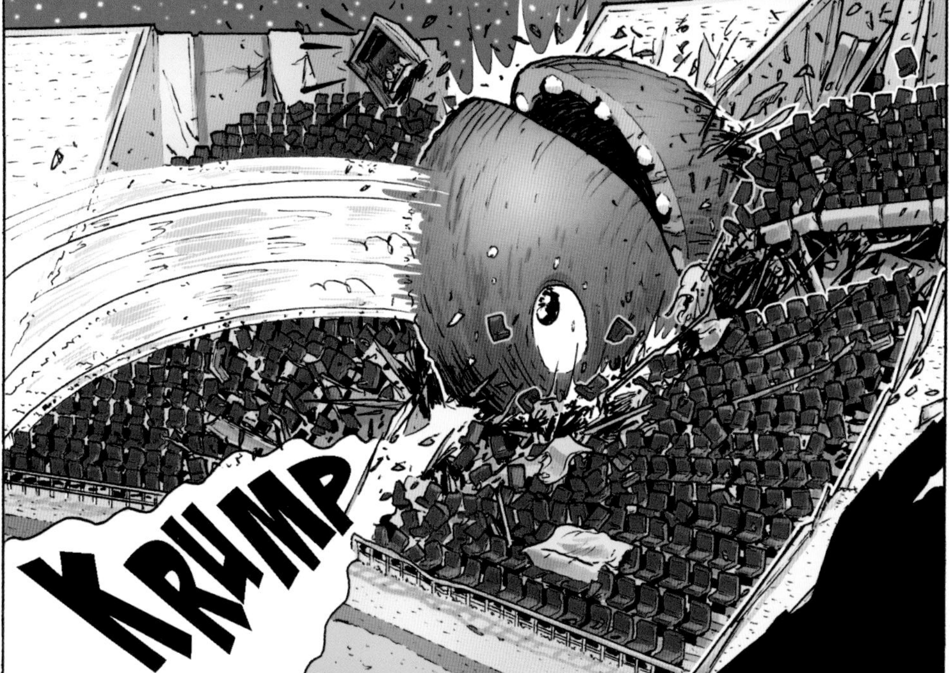
KRUMP

WE NOW GO LIVE FOR A PITCH-SIDE REACTION FROM LEGENDARY ONIONSKINS COACH, OXBLOOD JACKSON. OXBLOOD - ANY COMMENT?

BALLS.

ERM ... I'VE FOUND AN EXIT THAT'S NEITHER BLOCKED NOR GUARDED!

AND I THINK IT WOULD BE WISE TO BEAT A HASTY RETREAT BEFORE ANYONE TRIES TO PIN THIS NEW MESS ON US!

<SIGH>

WE NEARLY GOT CAUGHT BY A DEADLY MOB AND FOR WHAT? TO DISCOVER THAT THE OWNER OF THIS POOR LITTLE CASE ONCE SAT IN THE STADIUM! THRILLING BUT USELESS. I'M RUBBISH AT MY JOB...
NO YOU'RE NOT! YOU FOUND ME TODAY AND I WASN'T EVEN LOST!
AND ANYWAY YOU'RE WRONG, RANDALL. WE LEARNED SOMETHING VERY INTERESTING.
KICK

THE INSCRIPTION IN HUBERT'S SEAT READ: "FUTURE PROPERTY OF B.L."
H.BENNINGTON

B.L.? THAT SEEMS REALLY FAMILIAR...
AH, I MIGHT KNOW WHY!

TAKE A LOOK AT THIS CHILD'S DRAWING ON THE CASE!
a castle i wud like to liv in
B.L.
aged 7 3/4
TON
Park
IT'S THE SAME INITIALS? HMMM ... BUT I'M SURE I'VE HEARD THEM SOMEWHERE ELSE...

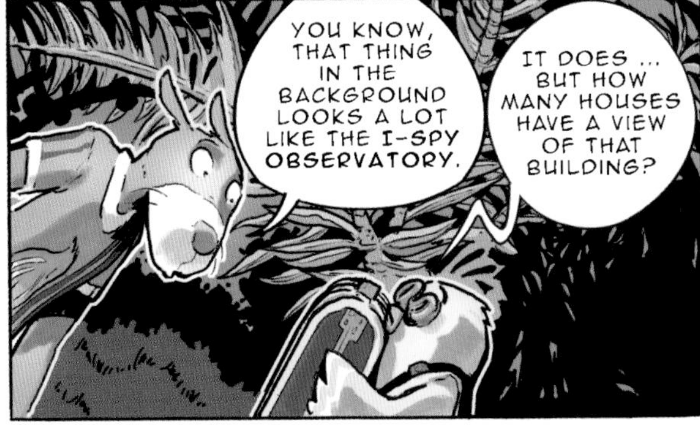
YOU KNOW, THAT THING IN THE BACKGROUND LOOKS A LOT LIKE THE I-SPY OBSERVATORY.
IT DOES ... BUT HOW MANY HOUSES HAVE A VIEW OF THAT BUILDING?

PLENTY, BUT NOT MANY WITHIN WALKING DISTANCE. DO YOU THINK THIS PLACE MIGHT BE REAL?

IF IT IS THEN THERE'S ONLY ONE STREET WITH TRIPLE ROOFS AND TRIANGULAR WINDOWS LIKE THAT PICTURE. CROTON ALLEY!
Croton Alley

GOOD ENOUGH FOR ME! WE'RE RUNNING OUT OF CLUES AND TIME - LET'S GO TAKE A PEEK AT THOSE HOMES.

WOW...

THIS IS SOME NEIGHBOURHOOD!
MICA, HOW MANY ROBOT TOYS DO YOU THINK I'D HAVE TO SELL TO GET A LITTLE PLACE UP HERE?
MORE THAN YOU CAN CARRY IN THAT COAT, LUCKY!

I ... I DON'T BELIEVE IT ... THIS IS THE HOUSE! IT LOOKS JUST LIKE THE PICTURE!
OH GOODY! I JUST HOPE THESE BIG GATES DON'T MEAN THERE'S ANOTHER BIG DOG WAITING TO POUNCE!

THAT'S NOT BAD FOR A SEVEN-YEAR-OLD ... NOT BAD AT ALL...

OKAY, SO HOW MANY ROBOT TOYS DO YOU THINK I'D HAVE TO SELL TO BUY THIS PLACE?

MOMENT OF TRUTH. LET'S SEE IF ANYONE'S HOME!
BRIIING
LOST & FOUND

WHAT'S WRONG WITH YOU PEOPLE?! DO YOU KNOW WHAT THE TIME IS?
ER, RANDALL, WE SHOULD GET INSIDE!

THAT'S WHAT I'M TRYING TO DO, TAW. ... COME ON...
RING RING RING
WELL, TRY HARDER!

WHAT? WHAT IS IT?! SPEAK UP!

BRONCO?

RANDALL!

SLAM

DID I MISS SOMETHING? GROUCHY BRONCO LIVES HERE?
BUT THAT CAN'T BE HIM! WE MUST HAVE THE WRONG HOUSE!

AT THIS MOMENT IN TIME ANY HOUSE WOULD BE THE RIGHT HOUSE!! WE HAVE GOT TO GET-

KRUNCH
I WARNED YOU, RANDALL!
OIF!

I GAVE YOU ONE LAST CHANCE AND THIS IS HOW YOU REPAY ME!
THUMP
LOST & FOUND

AND WHAT DO YOU LOT WANT?

WE ♥ ~~SPORT~~ MOB RULE!
WHAT DO WE WANT? ~~TROPHIES!~~ SCAPEGOATS WHEN DO WE WANT THEM? NOW!
MR LUTZ, I WOULD VERY MUCH APPRECIATE IT IF YOU'D HAND THOSE CRIMINALS OVER TO OUR LARGE ANGRY MOB! WE'D DEARLY LOVE TO GIVE THEM A NICE QUIET LYNCHING!
NOT A CHANCE – THEY'RE MINE! NOW EVERYONE GET OUT OF MY GARDEN! DON'T YOU HAVE A FINAL TO LOSE, OXBLOOD?
ER, ACTUALLY, HE'S ALREADY LOST IT.

NO LYNCHING ...
<SIGH>
HE REALLY IS INCREDIBLY GRUMPY...
I BLAME IT ON HIS LACK OF FITNESS.
STILL ... NICE LAWN THOUGH.
ANY FINAL WORDS BEFORE I FIRE YOU PERMANENTLY?
Y-Y-YES! I B-B-BELIEVE THIS L-L-LITTLE BAG M-M-MIGHT BE YOURS, SIR!

WHAT THE ... WHERE DID YOU FIND IT?
IN THE WAREHOUSE! IT'S THE OLDEST ITEM OF LOST PROPERTY WE HAD IN STORAGE!
LOST & FOUND

AFTER ALL THESE YEARS ... MY GRANDFATHER'S MISSING CASE!
THE INITIALS B.L. ... THEY STAND FOR BRONCO LUTZ! THAT'S YOU, ISN'T IT? YOU'RE B.L.

YES - HA, I STILL REMEMBER DRAWING THIS PICTURE! HUBERT USED TO BRING ME THIS WAY WHEN WE CAME TO SEE THE I-SPY OBSERVATORY. I THOUGHT THE HOUSE LOOKED LIKE A CASTLE!
B.L.
aged 7 3/4

IT'S THE MAIN REASON I BOUGHT THIS PLACE. NOW, COME ON IN AND LET'S HAVE A PROPER LOOK AT THIS THING!

FOR THE CRANKIEST CRANK IN TOWN, BRONCO SEEMS TO BE IN A GOOD MOOD!
YES ... IT'S UNNERVING!
THE WAREHOUSE ... HEHEHE ... IMAGINE THAT!

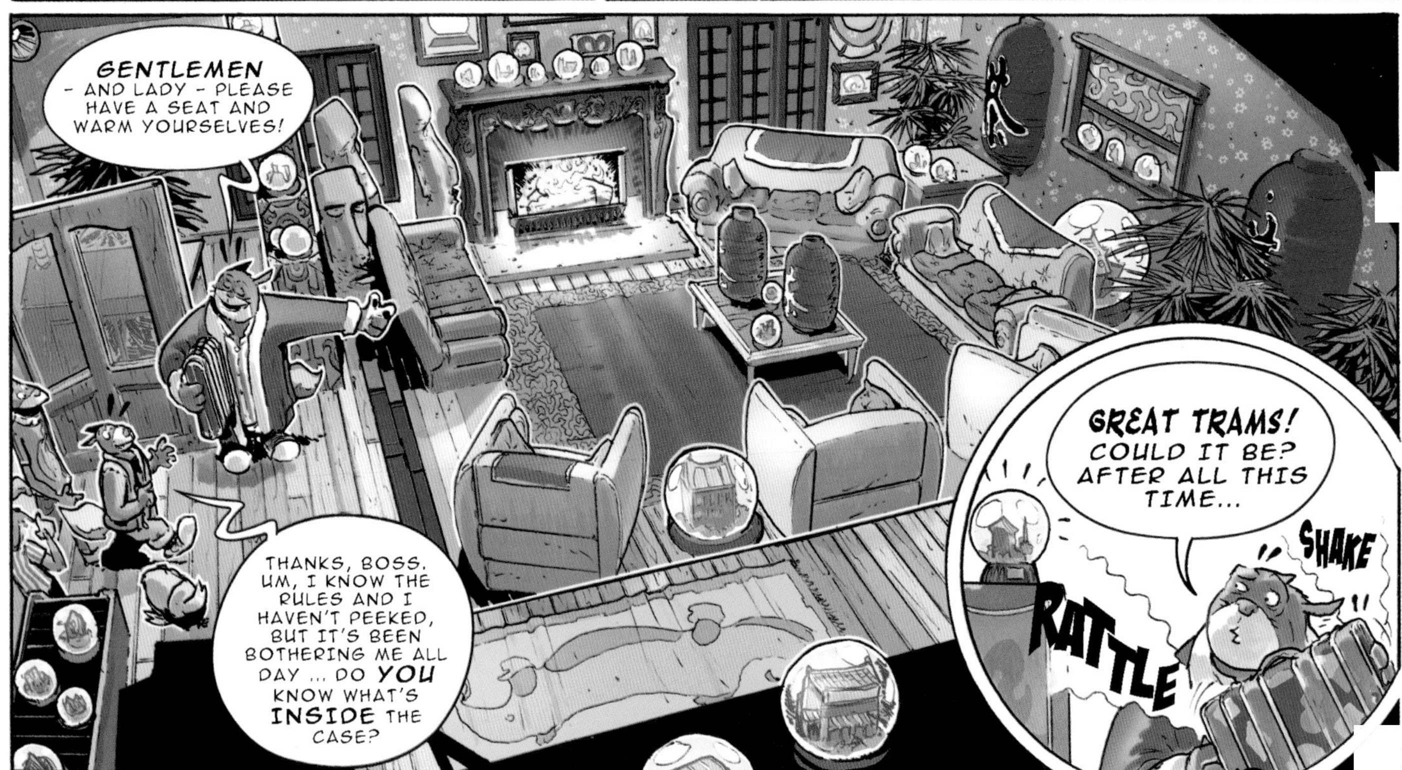
GENTLEMEN - AND LADY - PLEASE HAVE A SEAT AND WARM YOURSELVES!
THANKS, BOSS. UM, I KNOW THE RULES AND I HAVEN'T PEEKED, BUT IT'S BEEN BOTHERING ME ALL DAY ... DO YOU KNOW WHAT'S INSIDE THE CASE?
GREAT TRAMS! COULD IT BE? AFTER ALL THIS TIME...
SHAKE
RATTLE

THE HIDDEN ATTRACTION

A CASTLE AND A KEY? WHAT **WERE** YOU UP TO, GRANDFATHER?...
HEY, CAN I HAVE A QUICK WORD WHILE BRONCO'S DISTRACTED?

GUYS, I OWE YOU - I COULDN'T HAVE DONE ANY OF THIS WITHOUT YOUR HELP! BUT YOU'D BETTER NIP OUT THE BACK WHILE HE'S-
WHAT! ARE YOU TRYING TO GET RID OF US? JUST AS THINGS ARE GETTING *INTERESTING*?
YEAH - I'M NOT GOING *ANYWHERE!* YOU BOYS STILL OWE ME A MILKSHAKE STAND!

STOP BICKERING, CHILDREN, AND GATHER ROUND! THERE ARE THINGS THAT NEED TO BE SAID AND **I** NEED TO SAY THEM!

RANDALL, I KNOW WHAT KIND OF BOSS I'VE BEEN. I NEVER GOT OVER MY GRANDFATHER'S DISAPPEARANCE AND I TOOK IT OUT ON EVERYONE. ESPECIALLY YOU.
ONLY ON EVERY DAY OF THE WEEK WITH A '**Y**' IN ITS NAME!

TRUE, TRUE! BUT ALL THAT'S GOING TO CHANGE. NO MORE **MOODY BRONCO!**

I ALSO UNDERESTIMATED YOU AND THAT ERROR NEEDS TO BE CORRECTED. FIRSTLY, HERE'S YOUR BRAND NEW WORK-SHIRT, AS REQUESTED!
AT LAST! *DRIBBLE FREE!*

SECONDLY, I'VE A *NEW* ASSIGNMENT! YOU FOUR RETURNED THIS CASE TO ME IN A *SINGLE* DAY, WHICH MAKES YOU THE PERFECT TEAM FOR THE TASK.
SOUNDS EXCITING! SO WHAT WOULD THE JOB INVOLVE, BOSS?

WHY ... FINDING **THIS** PLACE, OF COURSE!

RIGHT... OKAY... ERM ... **TONIGHT?!**
WHEHEHE!
THE END?

UP

EGG
UP

THE ETHERINGTON BROTHERS
MONKEY NUTS
BOOK 1
The DIAMOND EGG of WONDERS
WELCOME TO THE *ISLA DE MONSTERA*, HOME OF THE WORLD'S ONLY TAP-DANCING, BANANA-LOVING, RUST-FIGHTING, COCONUT-TALKING, CRIME-BUSTING ORGANISATION...
MONKEY NUTS!
IN THEIR VERY FIRST ADVENTURE ***SID***, ***RIVET*** AND ***CHIEF TUFT*** ARE FORCED TO DO BATTLE AGAINST A HORDE OF RANDOM ODDBALLS AND WEIRDOS. WHEN A MYSTERIOUS SIGNAL BEGINS TO DRIVE THE LOCAL LOONIES INTO A CRAZY RAGE, THE MONKEY NUTS TEAM HAVE NO CHOICE BUT TO GRAB THEIR MASKS AND GET HEROIC!
MONSTER-CATCHING ACTION
FROM THE DFC LIBRARY!

More STORIES *from the* DFC LIBRARY

Collect them all!

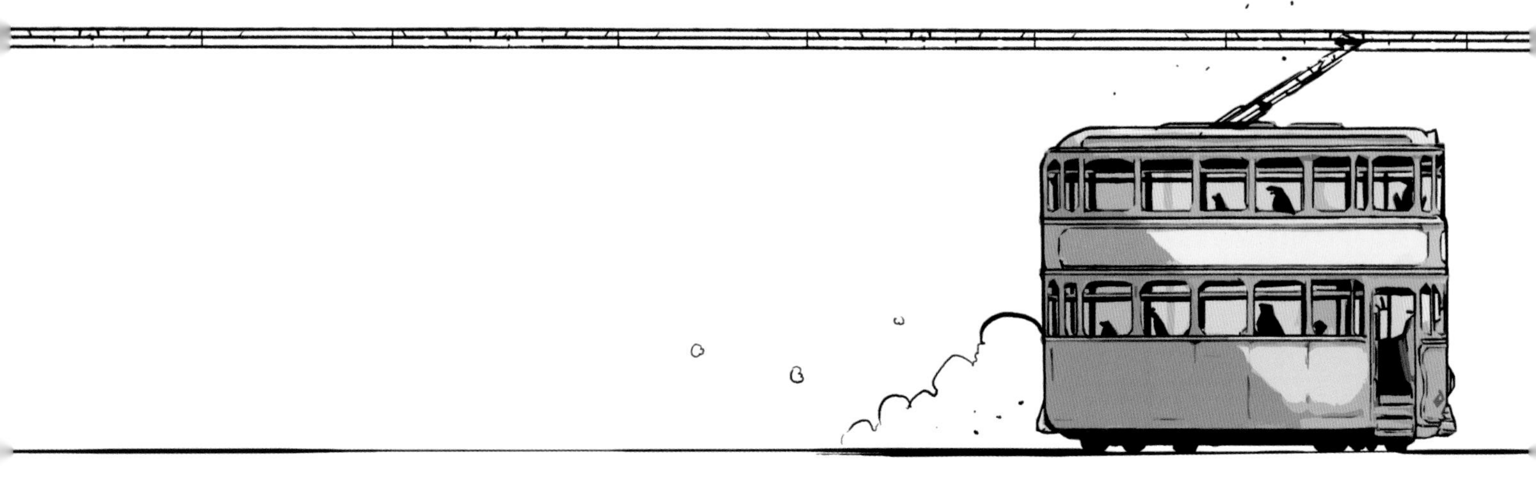

The DFC Library